中國古典藝藝

Stories of Chinese Wisdom

First Edition   2007
Second Printing   2008

Home Page:
   http://www.flp.com.cn
Email Addresses:
   info@flp.com.cn
   sales@flp.com.cn

ISBN 978-7-119-03404-1

Published by Foreign Languages Press
24 Baiwanzhuang Road, Beijing 100037, China
Printed by Beijing Foreign Languages Printing House
19 Chegongzhuang Xilu, Beijing 100044, China
Distributed by China International Book Trading Corporation
35 Chegongzhuang Xilu, Beijing 100044, China
P.O.Box 399, Beijing, China

Printed in the People's Republic of China

中國古典精萃

Stories
of
Chinese Wisdom

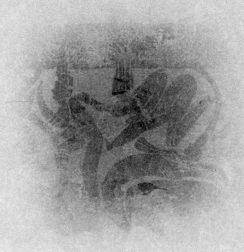

Ⓦ FOREIGN LANGUAGES PRESS

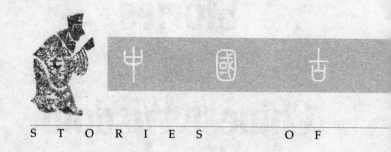

S T O R I E S   O F

CHINESE　　WISDOM

CONTENTS

CONTENTS

S T O R I E S   O F

中國古典智慧

CHINESE WISDOM

Lips and Teeth

Near the powerful State of Jin there were two small and weak states - Yu and Guo. Duke Xian, the ruler of Jin, decided to attack these poor neighbors. He ordered Xun Xi, a capable general, to carry out the task.

"We had better deal with one of them at a time," said the general. "Let us first try to make the duke of Yu allow our army to pass through his land on their way to Guo. He would agree if we bribed him with the best jade and the best steed in your possession."

Duke Xian was hesitant. "The best jade I have was left to me by my father, who loved it very much," he said. "And I use my best horse very often. Besides, the duke of Yu might accept our gifts without giving our army safe passage in return."

"That would not happen," said Xun Xi. "He would not take the things if he would not allow our army to pass. If he took them with a promise, your jade would only be moved from an inner room to an outer room, and your horse from an inner stable to an outer stable. There is nothing to worry about."

Duke Xian finally agreed. So Xun Xi went to Yu with the jade and the horse. On seeing the two things, the duke of Yu was delighted, and seemed ready to accept Jin's request. At this moment, Gong Ziqi, one of the duke's advisers, sounded a warning.

"The two states, Yu and Guo, are as close to each other as a man's lips and teeth," he said. "If the lips are gone, the teeth will be cold, for there is nothing to protect them. Guo has remained independent because Yu is there, and Yu has stayed intact because Guo is there. If we allow the Jin army to attack Guo by way of Yu, Guo will surely be vanquished. And if Guo falls in the morning, Yu will fall in the evening. So we should never allow the Jin army to pass through our land."

The duke of Yu, however, would not listen to this advice. He promised Xun Xi safe passage. What happened after that was predictable. It was easy for the general to conquer Guo with his overwhelming force. And it was just as easy for him to conquer Yu when he led his army back from Guo to Jin.

On the way, he did not forget to seize the jade and the horse he had presented to the duke of Yu and return them to the duke of Jin.

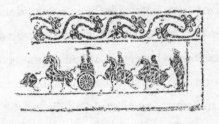

Controlling a Flood
by Blocking the River

Duke Li of Zhou was a despotic ruler. The people of the country hated him and cursed him. Shao Hu, a senior minister, said to him, "The people can no longer tolerate your harsh rule."

Duke Li was angry. He found a wizard from the State of Wei, and ordered the man to keep a close watch on those who would say bad things about him; whoever the wizard said had slandered him would be put to death. This silenced all the people of the country, who would only look at one another without saying a word when they met on the road.

Duke Li was satisfied. He said to Shao Hu, "I can stop all slander. No one is talking now."

"You have blocked the people's way of expressing themselves," Shao Hu replied. "But blocking the people's mouths is more dangerous than blocking a river full of water. If such a river is blocked, its banks will certainly collapse somewhere, and that will cause great damage. Blocking the people's mouths will produce a similar result. Therefore, one who manages a river should give an outlet to the water in it, and one who rules the people should give them opportunities to speak their minds."

"Big Sea Fish"

Tian Ying, the youngest son and prime minister of the ruler of the State of Qi, had the area of Xue as his fief. He wanted to build a city wall around the chief city of Xue. But many of his friends and assistants voiced opposition, saying that it was entirely unnecessary. Displeased, the prime minister told the receptionist of his official residence not to admit anyone who disagreed with him.

One man begged to see the prime minister, saying that he had only three words to say. "If I say one more word," he added, "I will accept the punishment of being thrown into a cauldron of boiling oil."

On hearing this remark, the prime minister agreed to receive the man, When the man was brought in, he confronted the prime minister, and said, "big sea fish!"

No sooner had he said those three words than he turned to go.

"Stay for a moment," said the prime minister.

"I will not risk the death penalty by saying more," the man protested.

"No death penalty for you," said the prime minister. "Explain your words."

"You must have heard about those big fish in the sea," the man said. "They are so big that nets cannot catch them and hooks cannot draw them up. But when they are stranded on dry land, they cannot even resist ants or crickets, which are free to gnaw at them."

"To you, the State of Qi," the man continued, "is what the sea is to those big fish. So long as you are protected by Qi, you have nothing to worry about. What is the use of a city wall in Xue? Should you lose the protection of Qi, a city wall in Xue, even though it were as high as the sky, would be of no use."

"You are right," the prime minister said. He thereupon gave up the idea of building a city wall in Xue.

How Zou ji Made the Duke of Qi Accept Criticism

Zou Ji, prime minister of the State of Qi, was tall and handsome. One morning, when putting on his official robe and hat, he looked into the mirror, and asked his wife: "How do I compare with Mr. Xu in the north of the city in appearance? Is he better-looking than I?"

"There is no comparison between Mr. Xu and you," she said. "You are far more handsome than he is."

Mr. Xu in the north of the city was known for his splendid appearance not only in the capital, but throughout the state. After hearing his wife's comment, Zou Ji was still not sure that he was more handsome than Mr. Xu. Later, he asked his concubine the same question, and she answered, "How can Mr. Xu compare with you?"

The next day, a guest came to see him. As they were chatting, Zou Ji asked the guest: "Between Mr. Xu and myself, which one do you think is more pleasing in appearance?"

"Mr. Xu is really good-looking," said the guest, "but he is not as handsome as you are."

On the third day, Mr. Xu was one of the visitors to the prime minister's residence. This gave the host a good opportunity to look carefully at the man he wanted to compare himself with. He came to the conclusion that Mr. Xu outshone him in features. Later he looked at himself in the mirror, and found the difference between them was quite obvious.

Lying in bed at night, he continued to think of the matter. Finally, he reached a better understanding of the whole thing. He said to himself: "My wife said fine words about me because she is partial to me; my concubine said fine words about me because she is afraid of me; and the guest said fine words

about me because he wants me to help him."

The next day, he was granted an audience with the duke of Qi. He said, "I know very well that, compared with Mr. Xu in the north of the city, I am not really handsome. But my wife, who is partial to me, my concubine, who is afraid of me, and my guest, who wishes me to help him, have all said that I am more handsome than Mr. Xu."

He continued, "Qi is a big state, with a hundred and twenty cities. No assistant of yours and no woman in your palace is not partial to you; no minister is not afraid of you; and no person within the borders of the state does not wish you to help him. In the light of my experience, it can be assumed that they are all trying to please you and conceal unpleasant truths from you."

"Well said!" the duke exclaimed. He then announced that anyone who could point out his faults to his face, whether he was a minister, an official, or a commoner, would be given the highest reward; anyone who would admonish him for doing something wrong would be given a medium reward; and anyone who talked about his weaknesses in public would be given a third-class reward.

In the days after this announcement, there were so many ministers and officials wishing to talk to the duke about his mistakes that his palace was as busy as a market place. A few months later, occasionally someone came to put forward a criticism or suggestion. A year later, people could no longer find fault with the duke, though they still wished to admonish him.

As Qi became well governed under this duke, other states, like Yan, Zhao, Han and Wei, vied with one another to pay homage to it. For Qi it was a great victory, a victory not won on the battlefield, but won within its court.

Buying Righteousness

Tian Wen, the powerful prime minister of the State of Qi, was known for his hospitality to people who came to him for help. At one time or another he sheltered thousands of men, among whom were scholars, warriors, clowns and thieves.

Once he put up a notice saying that he needed a man good at accounting to be sent to the region of Xue to collect debts people there owed him. One of the men then living under his protection wrote on the notice "I can go," and signed his name: Feng Xuan. On seeing these words, Tian Wen was a little surprised, for he had never talked with or even heard about this man. "This must be a capable guest I have," he said with a smile to his assistants, "I am sorry for not having treated him properly." He sent for Feng Xuan, asking him to come and see him at once.

When Feng Xuan came, Tian Wen said apologetically, "I am always tired and worried because I have to deal with all kinds of trifles. As I am a man of weak character and mediocre intelligence, I have been too bogged down in state affairs to show due respect to you. Is it true that you do not feel offended and are willing to go to collect debts for me in Xue?"

"Yes," Feng Xuan answered, "I am willing to go."

So horses were harnessed and luggage was put into the carriage Feng Xuan was to use. The most important things he took with him were the bamboo slips which recorded the debts. Paper had not been invented at that time.

Before leaving, Feng Xuan went to say goodbye to the prime minister, and asked, "What should I buy with the money collected in Xue?"

"Please buy what I am short of" was the reply.

Feng Xuan drove to Xue. He told the local officials to call together the people who were to pay back their debts. After the bamboo slips he had brought with him and those in the hands of the people had been matched and checked, he stood up and announced that, on orders from the prime minister, the money the people of Xue owed him would be given to them as a favor. In other words, all their debts were to be canceled. Furthermore, he had the bamboo slips burned there and then.

What a pleasant surprise this was for the people of Xue! To express their gratitude, they shouted, "Long live the prime minister!"

Feng Xuan drove straight back to the capital, without making a stop on the way. Early the next morning, he asked for permission to see the prime minister. Wondering why he had returned so soon, Tian Wen put on his official robe and hat, and received Feng Xuan.

"I did not expect you to return so early," said the prime minister. "Did you collect all the debts in Xue?"

"Yes, I did," Feng Xuan answered.

"What did you buy there with the money? "

"Before I left, you told me to buy in Xue what you were short of. I thought to myself that your mansions are filled with valuable objects, your kennels and stables are full of fine dogs and horses, and your halls and courtyards are lined with beautiful women. You are short of nothing but rightness. I ventured to buy righteousness for you."

"How did you buy righteousness? "

"The small region of Xue is your fief, but you did not think much of the well-being of the people there, let alone consider them as your children. On the contrary, you extorted profit from them like a merchant. I made so bold as to say to the people there that you had ordered me to free them from all their debts, and I had all the bamboo slips burned. For this favor the people there shouted, 'Long live the prime minister!' That was how I bought righteousness for you."

The prime minister was displeased. "You are dismissed, "he said.

A year later, the ruler of Qi suddenly said to Tian Wen: "I dare not use my father's ministers as my ministers."

The meaning was clear. So Tian Wen resigned and left the capital for his fief– Xue. When he was still about a hundred *li* away from Xue, he saw crowds of people from the region, old men and children among them, coming to meet him. Tian Wen turned to Feng Xuan and said, "Now I understand how you bought righteousness for me."

The Fox Borrows Power
from the Tiger

A tiger was hunting for small animals for food, when he caught a fox.

"How dare you seize me?" the fox demanded. "Don't you know that the Emperor of Heaven has made me the ruler of the animal kingdom? If you should hurt me, you would be defying the Emperor of Heaven. Please think of the consequence."

Seeing an expression of doubt on the tiger's face, the fox continued, "You think I am lying? Now let me walk around in the forest, and you follow close behind. You will see all the other animals flee in terror the moment they see me."

The tiger thought that this was a good test of the fox's claim. So he walked behind the fox in the forest. He was surprised to see that wherever he and the fox appeared, all the other animals ran away. He could not help but believe what the fox had said was true, and let the fox go free.

A Frightened Bird

During the Warring States Period (475-221 BC), there were seven major states in China, of which Qin was the most powerful and ambitious. The other six states tried to form an alliance against it, to better protect themselves. Chu, the largest of the six, naturally became their leader.

Once the State of Zhao sent an envoy by the name of Wei Jia to Chu to see its prime minister Huang Xie. During their conversation, Wei Jia asked Huang Xie: "Have you got competent generals?"

"Yes," Huang Xie said. "I intend to make General Lin Wu the commander of the allied forces."

At this, Wei Jia said, "I was keen on archery when I was young. May I draw an analogy between archery and your appointment of Lin Wu?"

"Please do," said the prime minister.

"Once the famous archer Geng Lei was talking with the duke of Wei at the foot of a high terrace. There were birds flying over them. Pointing to the birds, Geng Lei said, I can bring down a bird without shooting an arrow. A mere draw of the bow string will be enough.

" 'Is your archery as marvelous as that?' the duke asked, doubtfully.

" 'You will see, sire,' Geng Lei assured him.

"A moment later, a solitary wild goose came flying toward them from the east. Geng Lei twanged the string of his bow, and at the sound the bird fell to the ground.

"The duke was greatly surprised. 'You did bring down a bird without using an arrow,' he exclaimed in admiration. 'What a marvelous archer you are!'

"Then Geng Lei explained to the king how that had been possible.

" 'I knew the goose had been wounded by an arrow before I made it my target. It was flying slowly,

and crying sadly. It was slow because the old wound was still hurting; it was sad because it had been alone for a long time. It was a frightened, wounded bird. The sudden twang of my bow string startled it. It tried to soar upward, but the effort was too much for its old wound. And it fell.'

"That is the story. Now let me return to the question of your choice of a commander. General Lin Wu was once defeated and wounded during a campaign against Qin. Like a frightened wounded bird, he is not the right man to lead an army against Qin again."

Mending the Sheepfold
after the Sheep Have Escaped

Zhuang Xin said to Duke Xiang of the State of Chu: "On your left is the Marquis of Zhou; on your right is the Marquis of Xia; and following close behind your coach are the noblemen Xinling and Shouling. While paying no attention to state affairs, you indulge in extravagant pleasures and luxury. If things go on like this, the city of Yan, our capital, will be in danger!"

"Are you really old and muddle-headed," the Duke asked, "or do you take me as an ill omen for the future of the state?"

"I dare not point to any ill omen," Zhuang Xin said, " but I foresee what is certain to happen. If you continue to favor and trust those four men, the State

of Chu is doomed to fall. I beg you to allow me to go to the State of Zhao, where I will stay and watch the events in Chu."

So he went to Zhao, and stayed there for five months, until the State of Qin attacked and occupied several cities of Chu, including the capital. Duke Xiang fled to a place called Chengyang, from where he sent a courier to Zhao, to invite Zhuang Xin back, and the latter agreed.

On seeing Zhuang Xin again, the Duke said, "I am sorry for not listening to your advice. Now that such is the turn of events, what can be done?"

"Have you ever heard this popular saying?" Zhuang Xin answered, " 'It is not too late to call your dog when you see a rabbit, or to mend your sheepfold after your sheep have escaped.' In ancient times, King Tang and King Wu succeeded in ruling the whole country when the territory originally under their control was only a hundred *li* wide, while King Jie and King Zhou were vanquished though they had ruled the whole country. It is true that Chu

29

has become smaller, but if all the areas are put together, the periphery is still several thousand *li*, much larger than the size of the original lands of King Tang and King Wu."

How Rulers Should Love
Their Children

The Duke of Zhao died while his heir was still too young to govern the state. Government affairs were entrusted to the dowager, the late duke's wife.

Qin, a neighboring state, powerful and aggressive, made use of this opportunity to attack Zhao. The dowager begged Qi, another big state, for assistance. Qi set a precondition: the youngest son of late duke, Princess changlan, should be sent to Qi as a hostage.

The dowager, who dearly loved her youngest son, rejected this request, though her senior ministers kept urging her to agree. In her anger she proclaimed, "If anyone should come again to demand that I send my youngest son to Qi as a hostage, I will spit in his face!"

Chu Long, a veteran minister, begged to see the dowager. She granted him an audience, and waited for him in a sullen mood. After entering the hall, the old man tried hard to walk fast in spite of a crippled foot, for custom required one to walk fast towards a person superior in rank.

"I am sorry that I cannot walk fast," he said. "There is something wrong with my foot. That is why I did not come to pay my respects to you for such a long time. But I am afraid you may overwork yourself, so I wish to see you once in a while, even from a distance."

"I usually travel in my coach," said the dowager.

"Do you eat less than before?"

"I often eat porridge - that is my main food."

"For some time I had no interest in food. Then I forced myself to walk a few *li* a day. Gradually I ate more and more. This has been beneficial for my health." Chu Long said.

"I cannot do what you have done," the dowager, her irritated expression somewhat eased.

The old man continued, "May I mention my youngest son, Shuqi? I would not call him a promising boy, but as I am getting on in years, I cannot help loving him. Would you be kind enough to allow him to become one of the guardsmen of the palace?"

"Certairly," said the dowager. "How old is he?"

"He is fifteen. I wish to entrust him to your care before I die."

"Does a gentleman also love his youngest son?" asked the dowager.

"More than a woman does," the old man answered.

"That is not true. A woman may love her youngest son extremely dearly."

"But I thought you loved the duchess of Yan more than you loved Prince Chang'an", Chu Long

exclaimed. The queen mother's daughter, married to the duke of Yan, was living in that distant state.

"I am afraid you have overstated my love for the duchess of Yan. In fact, I love Prince Chang'an more." the dowager replied.

"Thereupon", Chu Long said, "Parents' love for their children is usually shown in their consideration for their children's future, especially their far-off future. When you saw the duchess of Yan off, you clasped her hands and cried, for she was going to a state far away from us. Even those who were standing by felt sorry for you. After she left, of course you missed her very much, but at each ceremony honoring your ancestors, you invariably prayed for her and said, 'May she stay in Yan for long!' Clearly you were thinking of her future, hoping that she would have sons and grandsons to rule Yan one after another. Am I right?"

"Yes," said the dowage.

Then Chu Long said, "May I ask you another question? Since Zhao became a dukedom, there have been three generations of rulers and noblemen. Are there, among the present noblemen, any descendants of the first duke?"

"Not to my knowledge."

"This does not mean that a ruler's descendants are all inferior to other people", the old man explained. "They often cannot maintain their positions because they attain high rank without making contributions and get rich rewards without doing real work. And they possess too many valuable objects. Now you have given Prince Chang'an a high rank, a large piece of fertile land, and many valuables, but you have not made him do good things for the state. Should you leave him one day, how could he keep his position in Zhao? So I thought you did not love him so much as you loved the duchess of Yan."

After a pause, the dowager said, "I understand what you want me to do. I will send him to any place you want him to go to."

On her orders, Prince Chang'an went to Qi with many assistants and attendants. And, as it had promised, Qi sent troops to Zhao to repel the attack by Qin.

Going South by Driving North

The ruler of the State of Wei decided to attack Handan, the capital of the State of Zhao. Ji Liang, one of his ministers, was on his way to another state when he heard of this. He returned at once, and hurried to see his master without changing his clothes or combing his hair.

"Your Majesty," he said, "on my way back I met a man driving his carriage northward, but he told me he was going to the State of Chu in the south.

"I could not help asking him, 'Since you are going to Chu, why are you driving north?'

"He answered, 'My horses are excellent.'

"I said, 'Your horses may be excellent, but the road you are taking does not lead to Chu.'

" 'I have brought plenty of money for travel expenses,' he said.

" 'But you cannot reach Chu by this road no matter how much money you have brought with you,' I pointed out.

" Then he added that he had a good driver. He did not know that the better his horses and his driver were, the farther he would be from Chu if he did not change direction.

"Your Majesty has the lofty aspiration of becoming the leader of all the states and winning the confidence of all their people. Your state is large and your armies are excellent. You think your territory will be further expanded and your position further elevated by attacking Handan. But such a step will only distance you from your ambition. It is like going to Chu by driving northward."

Buying a Dead Horse

When Duke Zhao began to rule the State of Yan, he was facing a difficult situation. Yan had just been defeated, and his father, the former ruler, had been killed, by the State of Qi. Determined to take revenge on Qi, the new duke did everything possible to recruit capable and virtuous men to help him. He decided to be modest, even humble, to such men, and was ready to give them money, houses, and other valuable things, so long as they could propose ways to make Yan strong.

One day he paid a visit to Guo Wei, a well-known scholar of his state.

"Qi made use of the confusion in Yan to launch a perfidious attack on us," he said to Guo. "I know very well that Yan is too small and weak at present to wreak vengeance on Qi. If anyone could help me to defeat Qi, I would be glad to share the rule of the state with him, for to avenge my father's death is now my greatest wish. How do you think I can find such a man?"

Guo Wei answered, "If you are sincere in looking for talented and virtuous men, and if you go to see them in person and treat them well, then learned scholars and brave warriors will come to you from all parts of Yan. They will come not only from Yan, but from other states as well. Your polite treatment of one such man will be as good as an invitation to all of them."

"Who should be the first one for me to visit?" the king asked.

"Before I answer this question," Guo Wei said, "I will tell you a story. There was once a king who wanted to have a good horse, one that could gallop a thousand *li* a day. Three years passed, and he did not find one. Then one of his servants volunteered to try to find a good horse for him. Only three days later, the servant returned to report that he had found a horse that could cover a thousand *li* a day. He said he had paid five hundred pieces of gold for it. The king wanted to see the horse at once, but the servant said it had died and he had brought back its corpse.

"This made the king furious. ' What I want is a live horse,' he shouted. 'What is the use of a dead one? And you paid five hundred pieces of gold for it!'

"The servant then said, 'When it is known that you were willing to buy a dead good horse for five hundred pieces of gold, all the people of the state will believe that you will buy a good live horse at any price. It is certain that extraordinarily fast horses will be brought to you in a short time.'

"The servant was right. Within a year, the king got three excellent horses. They were all able to run a thousand *li* a day.

"Now, if Your Majesty is really anxious to get capable people to help you, please begin with me. When it is known that Guo Wei is well treated and respected by Your Majesty, those who are wiser and abler man than I will come to serve you from far and near. They will not think that Yan is too distant to reach."

Duke Zhao took his advice. He had a magnificent mansion built for Guo Wei, and called Guo his teacher. This news spread all over Yan and to other states, and soon talented strategists and courageous warriors flocked to Yan. They worked together and in a few years made Yan powerful enough to attack and defeat Qi. Thus, Duke Zhao avenged his father's death.

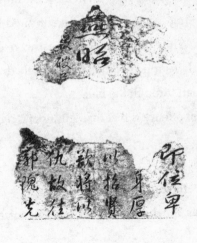

Oranges Change
with Their Environment

Yan Ying, a renowned minister of the State of Qi, was once sent to the State of Chu as an envoy. Before he arrived, the duke of Chu, who was proud of his own cleverness, had decided to do something to humiliate his guest, and had made the arrangements.

Yan Ying came, and the duke invited him to a banquet. While both host and guest were drinking merrily, there appeared two Chu officers dragging a bound man through the hall.

"What offence is that man guilty of?" demanded the duke.

"This man, from the State of Qi, was found stealing," the officers replied.

At this, the duke looked at Yan Ying intently, and

asked, "Are the people of your state prone to stealing?"

Yan Ying stood up, left his seat, and said very respectfully: "I have heard that orange trees south of the Kuai River produce very good oranges, while those north of the river produce a kind of fruit that is very small and tastes sour. The trees south and north of the river have the same foliage, but the fruit of the latter is so different that it can hardly be called oranges. What causes this difference? It is the difference in their natural environment, including water and soil. Now, people born and brought up in Qi do not steal, but after they come to Chu, they become thieves. Does Chu have an environment that turns good people into thieves?"

The duke laughed. "I should have known that a virtuous and learned man like you is not to be made fun of. I have only embarrassed myself," he said.

An Ointment for Chapped Hands

There lived in the State of Song a family good at making an ointment that could prevent the chapping of hands. For generations the people of the family had lived by washing and cleaning cotton fiber, and this ointment had protected their hands.

One day, a visitor came to the family. He said that he had heard about their ointment, and that he would offer a hundred pieces of gold for its prescription.

A family meeting was called. Many said that they had always been poor though they had worked hard. Now that there was an opportunity to get so much gold, it should not be missed, they insisted. So they agreed to sell the prescription.

With the prescription the visitor went to see the

ruler of the State of Wu, and explained to him what his secret ointment could do. At that time, Wu was under attack from the State of Yue. The ruler of Wu made the man commander of the Wu army. Then winter came, The Wu troops, their hands well protected by the ointment, won one battle after another, and finally defeated the Yue army. To reward the man, the ruler of Wu gave him a large fief.

The ointment worked in the same way in the family who made it and in the army the man commanded. With its help the family had washed cotton fiber but the man had got a fief. It was used in different ways for different purposes.

A Sick Man Who says He Is Well

The renowned physician Bian Que called on Duke Huan of the State of Qi. He stood watching the duke for some time, and then said, "I can see that you are ill. At this time your illness is between the skin and the muscle. It will certainly go deeper if you do not have it treated."

"I am not ill," the duke said. After Bian Que left, the duke scoffed, "Doctors are fond of calling a healthy man an invalid. They give such a man some treatment, and then boast of their medical skills."

Ten days later, Bian Que went to see the duke again. He said to the duke: "Your illness has entered the muscle. If you delay treatment, it will become more serious."

The duke made no response. Bian Que took his leave without more advice.

Another ten days passed before Bian Que visited

the duke for the third time. He said to the duke: "Your illness has encroached upon your stomach and bowels. If you refuse to have it treated, it will become more serious than before."

The duke again made no response, feeling deeply resentful about Bian Que's interference.

After another ten days, the doctor went to see the duke again. This time he turned to go the moment he saw the duke. The duke sent someone to ask him what he had to say. Bian Que answered, "When the illness is between the skin and the muscle, it can be cured by spreading hot medicinal herbs on the skin. When the illness is in the muscles, it can be reached by acupuncture needles. When the illness is in the stomach and bowels, medicinal liquids may be effective. But when the illness is in the marrow, the patient is in the hands of the god who controls life and death. There is nothing that doctors can do. As it is, the duke's illness is deep in his marrow, so I cannot cure him."

A few days later, the duke felt pain all over his body. He sent men to search for Bian Que, but the doctor had fled to the State of Qin. Soon after, Duke Huan died.

The "Foolish Old Man" Removes the Mountains

Mount Taihang and Mount Wangwu, which had peripheries of hundreds of *li* and were thousands of feet high, originally lay south of Jizhou and north of Heyang, or between the eastern section of the Great Wall and the Yellow River.

An old man of about ninety, who was called the "Foolish Old Man," lived north of the two mountains. They blocked his way to the south, and the old man and his family had to walk around them whenever they went in that direction. He was unhappy about this waste of time and energy.

One day, he called his whole family together and said to them,

"What would you say if I suggested all of us work

53

hard to level the two mountains so as to make it easy to go to places to their south?"

"A good idea!" his family chorused.

"Where could we dump the earth and rocks?" his wife asked.

"We might carry them to the shores of the Bohai Sea," said several people.

So they began. The old man, helped by his sons and grandsons, dug earth and broke rocks, which they carried in baskets to the shores of the Bohai Sea. The seven-year-old son of a widow, who was one of their neighbors, jumped at the opportunity to join them. They worked unceasingly on the mountains and returned home only when the seasons changed.

Not far from their place there was living an old man known for his wisdom, and was called the " Wise Old Man" by all who knew him. On hearing the news, he laughed and went to see the "Foolish Old Man",

"How silly you are!" he said. "You are so old and weak that you cannot even pluck the grass from the mountains, let alone the huge mountains themselves!"

The "Foolish Old Man" heaved a long sigh, and answered, "You think you are wise, but even a widow and a child understand things better than you do. When I die, there will be my sons, and they will have their sons and grandsons. Those grandsons will have their sons and grandsons. And this will go on forever. But the mountains will never grow any bigger. Why can we not level them?"

The "Wise Old Man" was at a loss for words.

The answer of the "Foolish Old Man" was heard by the mountain gods, who, in great fear, reported the whole thing to Lord of Heaven. Moved by the old man's determination, the Lord of Heaven ordered two gigantic deities to carry the two mountains on their backs and relocate them in places far from the old man's home. After that, there were no mountains between the eastern section of the Great Wall and The Yellow River.

Appraising a Horse

Duke Mu of the State of Qin wanted to have a good horse. He sent for Bo Le, a famous expert in judging horses. When Bo Le came, the duke said, "As you are rather elderly, I will not ask you to travel far and wide to look for a good horse for me. Can any one of your sons be entrusted with the job?"

"All my sons are capable of judging horses," Bo Le answered. "They can certainly discover good horses by looking at their appearances and feeling their bones and muscles. But none of them have the ability to find an superb horse, for its qualities are hard to grasp. You cannot even see the prints of its hooves, because it gallops fast and touches the ground only lightly. However, I have a friend who is as expert in this field as I am. I suggest you talk to

him. His name is Jiufang Gao."

The duke then summoned Jiufang Gao, and ordered him to find a steed that should be unequaled in the state.

Three months later, Jiufang Gao returned to report to the duke, saying that he had found an extraordinarily good horse. Asked to describe it, he said it was a brown mare.

The horse was brought to the duke, but it turned out to be a black stallion. Displeased, the duke called in Bo Le, and said to him: "The man you recommended cannot even tell a female horse from a male one, or a brown horse from a black one. And you said he could discover rare horses!"

Bo Le carefully examined the horse. Finally, he concluded that it was a horse of incomparably fine qualities, a horse the equal of which could not be found anywhere.

"Now I know Jiufang Gao's abilities are far greater than mine!" he said to the duke. "He observes the inner quality of a horse, and overlooks the outside appearance. He sees what he wants to see, and does not see what he does not want to see. He understands more than horses; he is able to get at the secret and mystery of nature."

Pulling the Elbow

Mi Zijian, one of Confucius' disciples, was appointed magistrate of Danfu by the duke of the State of Lu. Mi was afraid of one thing: His enemies might spread rumors and slanders about him, and the duke might believe them and, because of this, not trust him. Then it would be impossible for him to put his ideals into practice. With this fear in mind, when he went to say goodbye to the duke, he begged the latter to send two of his close assistants to work with him in Danfu, and the duke agreed.

On their arrival in Danfu, the local officials gathered to report to the new magistrate. Mi Zijian ordered the two men sent by the duke to write down what the officials said. After they began writing, Mi, who was sitting beside them, kept pulling and shaking their elbows, thus making it hard for the two men to write legibly. Mi then berated them for their poor handwriting. The two men were so unhappy that they asked Mi to allow them to return to the capital of the state.

"Go back as soon as possible," Mi said to them. "You write too badly to be useful here."

After the two men returned, they went to see the duke, saying that they had found it beyond them to work for Mi Zijian, the new magistrate of Danfu.

Surprised, the duke asked, "What happened?"

"The magistrate wanted us to write thing down," they answered, "but when we were writing, he frequently pulled and shook our elbows, so of course we could not write anything clearly. And he would fly into a rage at our illegible writing. The local officials thought this funny, and laughed at us. So we had to resign, and leave the place."

On hearing their report, the duke heaved deep sigh and said, "You do not know that Mr. Mi was hinting at my fault by pulling your elbows. I must have often disturbed him, and made it difficult for him to do what he wanted to do. If you had not come back to tell me about your experience in Danfu, I would continue to make the same mistake."

The duke then sent a trusted official to Mi Zijian, with this message: "From now on, Danfu no longer belongs to the duke, but to you. You are free to do whatever you feel is right for the place. There is no need to ask for my permission."

Catching Fish by Drying the Pond

Duke Wen of the State of Jin was making preparations for a battle at Chengpu against the State of Chu. He summoned Jiu Fan, his uncle and adviser, and said, "The Chu army is numerically superior to ours. How should we fight the battle?"

Jiu Fan answered, "A prince who is fond of decorum is never tired of formalities, and a prince who is fond of fighting is never tired of using stratagems. What you should do is use deceptive stratagems against the Chu army."

The duke then told Yong Ji, another assistant of his, what Jiu Fan had said.

Yong Ji said, "If you catch fish by drying up the pond, you can certainly get a lot of fish. But the following year there will be no fish in the pond. If you

64

hunt by burning the bushes and weeds in the marsh, you can certainly catch many animals. But the following year there will be no animals in the marsh. Deceptions and stratagems may be applicable for the time being, but cannot be repeated. They are not ways for constant use."

The duke thereupon adopted Jiu Fan's suggestions, as a result of which he defeated the Chu army at Chengpu.

After returning from the battle, the duke gave Yong Ji bigger reward than he gave to Jiu Fan. This aroused the discontent of the other assistants, who said,

"It was due to Jiu Fan's stratagems that we won the victory at Chengpu. But you put Yong Ji before him when you gave out rewards. Was this fair treatment?"

The duke said, "Yong Ji's advice will benefit us for a hundred generations, while Jiu Fan's idea was good for only one occasion or one event. Would it be right to consider one occasion more important than a hundred generations?"

Good Fortune or Misfortune

There was once an old man living on the north-ern border. One day, one of his horses ran away, and it could not be found though he looked for it far and near. On hearing about his, many of his neighbors expressed sympathy with him for the loss. But the old man said, "This may turn out to be a blessing."

A few days later, the horse came back of itself, and in addition brought a strange horse home with it. On this the old man was congratulated by his neighbors, but this time he said to them, "This may turn out to be a misfortune."

Now that he had a new horse, and a good one at that, his son soon took to riding. One day, while gal-loping happily on the horse, his son had a bad fall and broke his leg. Again, his neighbors came to say

comforting words to the old man, and they were surprised to hear him say, "Who knows, this may be a blessing."

A year later, fighting broke out near the border when some northern tribes started attacking the area. All able-bodied young men were ordered to take up arms and fight the invaders. Many of them died in battle. The old man's son, however, was exempted from military service, because he was crippled. Thus he survived the fighting.

The old man's story may be an illustration of the ancient philosopher Lao Zi's famous saying: "It is on disaster that good fortune perches; it is beneath good fortune that disaster crouches."

Planning Battles on Paper

In 260 BC, the State of Qin sent a huge army to attack the State of Zhao. The two armies faced each other near the city of Changping. Lian Po, a famous general who commanded the Zhao army, knowing that his opponent had superior forces, decided to keep the Zhao troops within fortifications, and strictly forbade them to sally forth to fight the enemy, though the latter repeatedly provoked them.

The Qin ruler knew that a long stalemate would be costly and dangerous. He then sent spies into Zhao to spread the rumor that the Zhao general Qin was most afraid of was not Lian Po, but Zhao Kuo. Zhao Kuo was the son of a capable general called Zhao She, who had died.

When he was young, Zhao Kuo had studied

books on military strategies and tactics. He was so proud of his knowledge in this field that he looked down upon all other strategists of his day. During discussions of military affairs with his father, he talked expertly, and the veteran commander often could not find any mistakes. But the father never gave the son a word of praise. His mother had once asked the old general what he thought of their son. The answer was: "Fighting on the battlefield means danger and death, but Kuo talks about it casually, as if it was nothing serious. It would be well if he was not made a commander. If he was, he would be the man to lead the Zhao army to destruction."

When the duke of Zhao heard the rumor that Qin was most afraid of Zhao Kuo, he made Kuo replace Lian Po as the commander of the Zhao army. Before Kuo left for the front, his mother wrote to the king, begging him not to use her son. The king then summoned her, and asked her why she disagreed with the decision. She said, "His father was the commander when I was married to him. I saw him taking food and drink to dozens of men whom he respected like teachers, and treating hundreds of men like friends. He distributed among his subordinates all the good things Your Majesty and the royal family had given him. And he never gave a thought to family affairs after he was entrusted with an important duty. But Kuo is different. Since he was appointed the commander, he has always sat in the seat of honor when he receives army officers, who dare not lift their eyes to look at him. He has stored at home all the gold and silk Your Majesty has given him. And he has been busy looking for and buying land and houses. That is how he is different from his father. I beg Your Majesty not to send him to the front."

"Please say no more about this," the king said. "The decision will not be changed."

After he took over, Zhao Kuo changed all the arrangements Lian Po had made, and appointed many new officers. When the Qin commander got this information, he secretly deployed part of his forces behind the Zhao army. Then he attacked. As expected, Zhao Kuo ordered his men to go out of their fortifications to meet the enemy. The Qin troops withdrew, as if they could not hold their ground. Zhao Kuo pursued, and was soon surrounded and cut off from his supplies. About forty days later, all his men were starving and demoralized. Zhao Kuo decided to fight to break through the encirclement with a group of crack soldiers. In the fighting he was killed. After that, his army surrendered, and the State of Zhao lost tens of thousands of men.

Lord She's Love for Dragons

Zi Zhang, one of Confucius' disciples, went to see Duke Ai of the State of Lu. He had heard that the duke respected wise scholars, and would use them in his government or at least listen to their views on government. But, having waited for seven days without getting an audience, he decided to leave Lu. Before leaving, he asked someone to pass on the following message to the duke: "Your humble servant heard that Your Excellency was fond of scholars, so he came from a thousand *li* away, in spite of frost and dew, dust and dirt, to seek an audience. However, he never got an opportunity though he has been waiting here for seven days. Perhaps Your Excellency is fond of scholars in the same way as Lord She was fond of dragons.

"Lord She, whose name was Zi Gao, was a noble-man of the State of Chu. He loved dragons so much that he had images of dragons carved on many things he used, such as hooks and wine cups, and on the walls of his rooms. A real dragon heard about this, and decided to pay him a visit. It came down from the clouds to his house. It stuck its head in through Lord She's study window, leaving its tail in the courtyard. At the sight of a real dragon, Lord She was frightened out of his wits. He turned and ran away as quickly as he could, his face pale and his heart beating fast. It was clear that what Lord She loved was not real dragons, but things that looked like dragons.

"Now Your Excellency would not receive a scholar who had traveled a thousand *li* to see you. And you are reputed to be fond of scholars. It is clear that the people you are fond of are not real scholars, but those who only look like scholars."

The Cock and the Swan

Tian Rao had been working for Duke Ai of the State of Lu for some time, when he decided to leave. He felt that the duke did not understand him and would not entrust him with important duties: so he went to see the duke one day, and said,

"I will leave you, and fly away like a swan."

"Why?" the duke asked.

"Consider the cock, sire," replied Tian Rao. "With a red comb on its head it looks very elegant. The sharp claws on its feet make it fierce. When fighting an enemy, it is exceedingly brave and never retreats. On seeing food, instead of enjoying it alone, it is kind enough to call on its companions to join in the feast. It never fails to crow at dawn to wake people up. Although it has these five merits-elegance, militancy, bravery, humanity and trust worthiness-Your Excellency may want to have it killed and stewed for food.

Why? Because it comes from a place near you and is always around you."

"A swan is different," Tian Rao continued. "It can easily fly a distance of a thousand *li*. When it comes, it may take a rest in your gardens or ponds, eat your fish or shrimps, and peck at your millet and corn. It does not have any of the five merits that a cock has. But you think highly of it, and will not allow anyone to harm it. Why? It is mainly because it comes from far away. So I will fly away like a swan," Tian Rao concluded,

"Please stay," the duke said. "I will write down what you have just said."

"What is the use of that? When there is a capable scholar in a state, the important thing to do is to give him an opportunity to show his talents."

Then Tian Rao left for the state of Yan, where he was made the prime minister. Three years later, Yan had become a peaceful and well-governed state, cleared of thieves and robbers.

When Duke Ai of Lu heard about this, he was deeply remorseful. "Where can I find another Tian Rao?" he reproached himself. He showed his regret by reducing his enjoyments and lowering the level of his daily supplies.

The Cicada, the Mantis
and the Oriole

The ruler of the State of Wu was making preparations for an attack on the State of Chu. To prevent his assistants from voicing disapproval, he said publicly, "Anyone who wants to stop me shall be put to death!"

One young official thought his decision unwise, but dared not protest. Carrying some stones and a slingshot, he sauntered in the back garden of the palace early in the morning for three days. His clothes were wet with dew. The ruler saw him, and said, "Come over here. Why have you made your clothes so dirty?"

The young official said, "On a tree in the garden there was a cicada. It kept crying sadly and drinking

dew on that high place, unaware that a mantis was just behind it. The mantis arched its back, and stretched out its front legs, intending to catch the cicada, not knowing that an oriole was close beside it. The oriole straightened its neck ready to peck at the mantis at any moment, but it did not know that a stone would soon be shot at it from a slingshot. These three things-the cicada, the mantis and the oriole-were all eager for gains that lay before them, but were ignorant of the danger that perched behind them."

Upon hearing this, the ruler of Wu canceled the attack on Chu.

A Warning Ignored

During the Western Han dynasty (206 BC-AD 23) a general by the name of Huo Guang was so powerful that he controlled the government for a long time. Arrogant and extravagant, he made the other officials in the court fear and hate him, but no one dared oppose him openly. Xu Fu, an ordinary scholar, saw danger in Huo's behavior to the state and to the general himself. He wrote several memorials to the emperor, saying that Huo's power should be curbed, so as to prevent him from bringing about his own destruction. But the emperor ignored this warning.

After the general's death his descendants were even more ambitious. They planned to have the emperor deposed. This attempt, however, failed in the end, and all those involved in it were killed on orders from the emperor. Those who had detected and revealed the crimes of the Huo family were given due rewards.

Then the emperor received a memorial which began with a story:

"Once a man paid a visit to a friend of his. The man happened to see that firewood was piled near his friend's stove. He immediately advised his friend to move the firewood away from the stove. Otherwise, he warned, a fire might break out in the kitchen. But his friend did nothing about the kitchen.

"Not long afterwards, a fire did break out in the friend's kitchen. Thanks to the help given him by his neighbors and friends, the fire was put out before it caused too much damage. To express his gratitude to them, he prepared a feast with much

wine. Those had suffered burns in fighting the fire were given the seats of honor, and others were seated in accordance with their contributions.

"One guest said to the host, 'It would not have been necessary for you to prepare this feast and buy wine if you had listened to the friend who suggested moving the firewood away, for there would not have been a fire at all. It is right that today you should be treating all those who helped to save your house, but is it right to forget the friend who gave you that important suggestion?'

"The host realized his mistake, and invited that friend to the feast at once."

"About the possibility of the Huo family causing trouble," the memorial continued, "Xu Fu submitted several memorials to Your Majesty recommending precautions. If some measures had been taken, neither the state nor the Huo family would have suffered such great losses. Now that the incident is over, Xu Fu is not among those rewarded. I beg Your Majesty to give the matter further consideration."

The emperor accepted this advice. He gave Xu Fu ten bolts of silk as a reward, and later appointed him an official in the government.

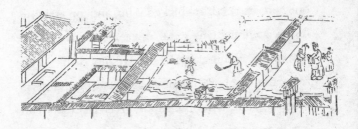

Cutting the Silk on the Loom

A young man called Le Yangzi, while walking along a road, happened to see a piece of gold someone had dropped. He picked it up, and, on arriving home, gave it to his wife. She said, "I have heard that men with high aspirations will not drink water from the Robbers' Spring, because the name is offensive, and will refuse food given to them in an insulting manner. Do you think they would pick up lost things, though they were valuable?"

Yangzi was ashamed. He threw the gold away and, determined to study, went to a good teacher in a distant place.

One year later, he returned home. His wife asked what had made him come back.

"I was homesick," he answered.

Taking a knife and walking to the loom, his wife said, "This piece of silk is made of thread from cocoons. First the thread is put on the loom. Then an inch of silk is woven. Inch after inch is added, finally a piece of silk will be completed. If what has been woven is broken, all the work that has been done is lost, and all the time that has been used is wasted. As a student, you should learn something new every day, so as to make your learning complete and your character perfect. Now you have returned home halfway through your studies. Is that in any way different from cutting the silk on the loom before it is finished?"

Deeply moved by her words, Le Yangzi left at once to resume his studies. It was another seven years before he returned home again.

Camel Guo the Tree Expert

Camel Guo's original name is unknown, but since he had a big hump on his back and walked with his back bent, like a camel, he was generally called "Camel Guo ".

He lived in a village not far from Chang'an, the capital. As he was an expert at planting trees, rich people in the city who had gardens or orchards vied with one another in inviting him to their homes and asking him to plant or transplant trees. All the trees he had planted would live and grow very well, and bear fruit quickly. Other planters who had watched and imitated his way of planting trees were never as successful as he was.

When he was asked why he did so well with trees, his answer was, "I cannot make trees live or bear fine fruit. I can only do things according to their nature, and help them to live in a way required by their nature."

"When you plant a tree," he further explained, "you should let its roots spread out freely. Old earth should be used around them, and the new earth added on top should be made compact. When this is done, do not disturb the tree any more, and do not worry about it. While planting it, handle it carefully as if you were nursing a baby; after planting it, just leave it alone as if you had thrown it away. In this way you make it possible for the tree to enjoy its own nature and grow as it naturally grows. So what I can do is to do nothing to hamper its growth, not to make them grow fast or bear fruit too early."

"Other planters," he continued, "love their trees too dearly and worry about them too much. They go back to look at their trees in the morning, and return to feel them in the evening. Moreover, they cut the bark to see if they are still living, or shake the trunk to see if they are still standing firm. In this way, they drive their trees farther and farther away from their nature. They intend to love their trees, but in fact they harm them. That is why the result of their work is not as good as that of mine."

"Can your way of planting trees be applied to officials' way of governing the people?" someone asked.

"I only know something about planting trees," Camel said. "Governing the people is not my business. But in my village, the officials give orders too often. They seem to have pity on the people, but in effect they do harm to them. In the mornings or in the evenings, officials shout their orders in loud voices, 'Sow seeds! Go harvesting! Raise silkworms! Weave cloth! Nurse your children! Look after your chickens and pigs! ' They often beat drums to bring the people together. We common people sometimes have to stop eating our meals to listen to or entertain the officials. We are made busy and tired. How can we live in peace or in a way suited to our nature? Maybe here is some similarity between planting trees and governing the people."

"Well said!" the one who had asked the question exclaimed. "I have asked about tree planting, but I have learned something about government: Camel's experience should be made widly known for the reference of the officials."

A Good Swimmer

Most men in Yongzhou Prefecture used to be good swimmers. Once, the Xiang River, which flows through the area, was high and swift. A few men were crossing it in a small boat. They were just in the middle of the river, when an accident happened. The boat capsized, and started to sink. All the passengers had to plunge into the water to try to swim to the opposite bank.

One of them, known as an excellent swimmer, was swimming very slowly, though he was making great efforts. He was gradually lagging behind his companions, who were wondering what trouble he had got into.

"Why are you so slow?" one of them asked him. "You swim much better than we do."

"It is because I have tied more than a thousand coins to my belt," he answered. "They are heavy. With this heavy load, I cannot swim quickly."

"Why not throw them away?" the others said.

The man shook his head without saying anything, a pained look on his face.

Some time later, all the other people had reached land, but this man was still struggling in the river, his strength fading quickly. His friends, who were now standing on the bank were greatly worried about him.

"Throw away your money at once!" they shouted. "Do not be a fool. What would be the use of the money if you were drowned?"

Again the man shook his head. A moment later he sank.

When I heard the story, I felt sorry for the man who would rather be drowned than give up his money. Truly, in certain situations, one's love of money and one's death may be deplorably connected.

A Donkey in Guizhou

At one time, there were no donkeys in Guizhou. A certain man who enjoyed doing odd things transported one by boat into the area. But he found no use for it there, so he let it go free at the foot of a mountain.

A tiger happened to see it. Impressed by its huge size, the tiger thought it was a deity. The tiger hid among some trees, and peeped at it. Some time passed, the tiger, still not knowing what it was, moved out of the trees, and walked closer to it, with caution and respect.

One day, the donkey brayed. The tiger was greatly frightened, thinking that the donkey was going to devour it. Gradually, the tiger became accustomed to the donkey's brays. While walking back and forth, the tiger kept a close watch on the donkey, without discovering anything unusual about it. Then the tiger moved round it at a short distance, attempting to tease it and provoke it by knocking against it. The donkey was uncontrollably furious, and kicked the tiger with its foot.

This delighted the tiger. "That is all it can do!" the tiger said to itself. It leaped on to the donkey with a loud cry, broke its neck, and ate all its flesh before going away.

A Lesson About Taking Medicine

Once I was seriously ill. The most delicious food was tasteless to me, and a high fever made me feel as if my body were burning. A friend happened to stop by, and, on hearing about my illness, said, "You must try to find a good doctor at once. There is one near my place. I know he once cured a patient with a bad case of scabies and made him healthy and handsome. He also treated a patient with a leg disease, and turned him into a fast runner. Your disease would seem common to him and present no difficulty at all. If I were you, I would go and see him without delay."

I accepted his advice, and went to see the doctor. After feeling my pulse, examining the color of my face and tongue, and listening to my voice, he made a diagnosis: "Your disease has been caused by an im-

proper arrangement of work and rest, and lack of attention to your food and clothing. The result is that your stomach cannot digest what you have eaten, and your vital organs cannot coordinate their functions as they should. So your body is just like a useless bag. But do not be worried; I have ways to deal with your condition."

He took out some medicine, handed it to me, and said, "This medicine will put you at ease by doing away with your agitation, and restore the proper working of your organs. When the main cause of your illness is removed, you will be able to replenish the energy and blood you have lost."

"But remember," he added, "this medicine has a little poisonous element in it. Stop taking it as soon as you feel better. An overdose of it will upset the harmony of your physical and mental conditions."

I returned home, and began taking the medicine. Two days later, my legs seemed much lighter, and I could walk faster than before. My fever, together with the numb feeling in my body, was gone. Ten days later, I was no longer itching all over. A month later, my eyes became sharp enough to perceive the tiniest objects, and my ears sensitive enough to catch the weakest sounds. Walking on rough ground was as easy to me as walking on a smooth floor, and coarse food became as tasty as choice delicacies.

My wonderful recovery brought many friends to my home. They congratulated me, and gave me all kinds of suggestions. Among them one sounded particularly wise and helpful: "The medicine you have taken is really marvelous! It is magical! It was good luck that you got such effective medicine. But we all know that doctors usually use only part of their skills and leave their patients only partly cured. The purpose is clear: They want their patients to continue asking them for help so that they can continue getting money. What you should do at this moment is ask your doctor for more of the same medicine, and then you will make a thorough recovery and will be even healthier than you are."

"The doctor may have played a trick," I said to

myself after I heard this advice. "The medicine has done me a great deal of good, and of course the more I take of it, the better the result will be." So I got more of it.

Five days later, the poisonous effect of the medicine exploded with violent force. I suffered from fever and cold like a malaria patient. This reminded me of what the doctor had warned at the beginning. I hurried to his place, and begged for his help.

"So you did not understand my words," he said, surprised and displeased. But he prepared an antidote for me. I took it, and a few days later I recuperated.

The Dragon in the Pond

Once there was a dragon breeder who knew very well what a dragon desired and enjoyed. In his court-yard was a pond filled with water, in which he kept a dragon, and gave it very delicious food. Now it lay still on the bottom of the pond for a rest, now it swam a little in the water when it wanted to stir. Life was so satisfying to it that it never thought of the sea, where it had come from.

One day, it happened to see a wild dragon flying over its pond. Happily, it greeted the flying one, and said, "What are you busy with? Between the vast earth and the boundless sky you have to keep flying to look for food in the warm season, and try to find a place which you can use as a shelter in the winter. How can you be free from fatigue and worries? Why not come and stay with me? I wish to have company. A free and easy life is waiting for you here in this pond."

Smiling, the wild dragon answered, "How narrow-minded and short-sighted you are! Nature has given us a good form-two horns on the head and scales on the body. It has given us admirable abilities-to dive into water and soar into the sky. It has given us skills - to blow the clouds about and ride on the wind. It has also given us duties - to restrain the proud and moisten the dry and withered. What corner of the universe have I not been to, and what change in it have I not witnessed? There is no happiness greater than this!"

"But you have confined yourself in a bog," the wild dragon went on, "surrounded by mud and sand,

accompanied by leeches and eels. You get the leftovers of your breeder's meals, and think they are the best food in the world. Although we are similar in appearance, we have entirely different interests and goals."

"But remember," the wild dragon said in conclusion, "that which is kept and fed by somebody will eventually be disposed of in one way or another. I have pity on you, and wish to get you out of this shameful and dangerous condition. But you enjoy your life here. It is clear that you will not escape a tragic end."

The wild dragon left. Shortly afterwards, the dragon in the pond was killed by its breeder, and chopped into mincemeat for food.

A Child Prodigy

Near my hometown there was a child by the name of Fang Zhongyong. His father and grandfather were farmers. Before he was five years old, he had never seen writing brushes or ink sticks, for his family, being illiterate, had never owned or used them. One day, he surprised his father by suddenly asking for those things, and after being told that they were not available at home, insisted on having them. His father had to borrow the tools for writing and some paper from a neighbor. Holding the brush in his hand, the child wrote four lines of verse, expressing his love for his parents, and signed his name under them.

Soon the story was heard by all his neighbors; moreover it attracted some educated people in the

area to his home. They would point at an object and asked the boy to write a poem about it. In a moment, the boy would compose a few lines with a clear idea. This aroused the curiosity of many people in the county, who would invite the child and his father to their homes, or ask the child to write something, and give him a little reward. To the father this was a quick and easy way of making money, so he took the child to people's homes every day, giving him no time or facilities for study.

I heard stories about this gifted child a long time ago. One year I returned home, and met him at my uncle's place. He was then twelve or thirteen years

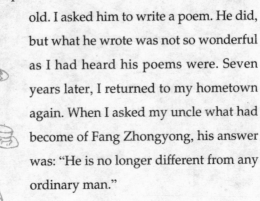

old. I asked him to write a poem. He did, but what he wrote was not so wonderful as I had heard his poems were. Seven years later, I returned to my hometown again. When I asked my uncle what had become of Fang Zhongyong, his answer was: "He is no longer different from any ordinary man."

Borrowing a Ladder in a Polite Way

In the State of Zhao there was a nobleman called Chengyang Kan. Once, his house caught fire, and it was necessary to climb on to the roof to fight it. He did not have a ladder, so he ordered his son, Chengyang Nu, to go and borrow one from his friend Ben Shui.

A young man who considered decorum most important, Chengyang Nu took some time to pick a hat and a robe suitable for formal occasions, and then walked unhurriedly as a man of his status should. When he finally arrived at Mr. Ben's home, he bowed three times to his host before he agreed to enter the hall. Mr. Ben told his servants to prepare a feast. Various dishes, including salted pork and pork stewed in soy sauce, were brought to the table, Wine was also served. After drinking a little from his cup, the young man stood up, holding his cup in his hand, to invite his host to drink, so as to show his respect for his father's friend.

When all these formalities had been duly performed, Mr. Ben Shui said, "Today you have condescended to honor my shabby hut with your presence. You certainly have instructions to give me. May I ask what they are?"

Only then did Chengyang Nu explain the purpose of his visit. "Heaven has let a disaster befall my home," he said. "A fire has unexpectedly broken out, and it is becoming worse and worse, threatening to destroy the whole house. The best way to extinguish it, we suppose, is to pour water on it from the roof. But we cannot get on to the roof, for we do not have wings. Up there we have heard that among your possessions is a ladder. Will you be kind enough to lend it to us?"

On hearing this, Mr. Ben Shui stamped his feet in exasperation, and cried, "You are so pedantic! You are so pedantic! If a man is eating something on a mountain when he sees a tiger, he must throw out the food in his mouth and start running away at once. If a man is washing his feet in a river when he sees a crocodile, he must leave the place instantly, even without his shoes on. Your house is burning. Is it time for you to observe the formalities?"

In a great hurry Mr. Ben took his ladder and ran with the young man to his friend's place. When they arrived, the whole house had been reduced to ashes.

The Orange-Seller's Talk

In Hangzhou there was a fruit-seller who was exceptionally adept at storing oranges. Neither the cold of winter nor the heat of summer could do any harm to the oranges he kept. Whenever they were taken out, they were attractively shiny, with golden or silvery skins. But the inside was usually as dry as old cotton.

Puzzled, I could not help asking the seller: "Can the oranges you sell be placed on altars as offerings to gods and ancestors? Can they be used to treat guests? Or are they intended to fool people with their beautiful appearances? Is the trick you play not too dishonest and deceptive?"

On hearing my questions, the fruit-seller frankly laughed. "I have been engaged in this business for

quite a few years," he said. "I earn a living in this way. I sell my fruit, and people buy it. I have never heard anyone complaining about it. You are the only one who is unhappy about and critical of my way of doing things."

"Am I the only one in the world who plays tricks on or deceives other people?" he went on. "Have you ever thought of this, my friend? Just think of those military commanders who sit in big chairs covered with tiger skins with a sword symbolizing authority beside them. They look powerful and intimidating, as if they were going to fight the enemy. Can they work out effective strategies for the defense of the country? Will they go to the front if the country is attacked? And those wearing high official hats and wide official belts behave like officials with wisdom capable of running the government. Can they do anything good for the common people? When robbers run wild, they do not know how to suppress them. When the common people find life hard, they do not know how to give them relief. They cannot prohibit their subordinates from committing crimes; they cannot strengthen the rule of law when law is ineffective; and they waste the state's funds without any feeling of shame. They live in magnificent mansions, and ride on fast steeds. They are fat with big bellies, because they drink tasty wines and eat delicious foods every day. They appear dignified, serious and awe-inspiring. But in fact, like the oranges I sell, they are all golden and silvery on the outside, but rotten like old cotton on the inside. I hope you will examine these people instead of my oranges."

I was silent, for I could not think of a proper answer.

The Scholar and the Wolf

Zhao Jianzi, a nobleman of the State of Jin, was hunting in the region of Zhongshan. Guided by men managing the mountains and woods, and helped by fierce hawks and hounds, he had killed a great number of wild animals and birds with his arrows. All of a sudden, he saw a wolf standing on its two hind legs in the middle of the road, howling. He picked out a sturdy arrow, put it to his string, and shot the wolf with it, The wolf uttered a loud cry and ran away. The nobleman drove his chariot in hot pursuit of the wounded animal. The dust raised by his chariot was so thick that things ten steps away could not be seen clearly.

At this moment, Mr. Dongguo, a scholar who believed in the Mohist philosophy of universal love, was on his way to Zhongshan, where he intended to seek a government post. With him was a lame donkey carrying a big box of books on its back. Out of the cloud of dust emerged a wolf. It stopped in front of him, and said in a sad voice: "Mr. Dongguo, you are known for your devotion to the well-being of the poor and the wretched. Now I am in great danger. I will certainly be killed if I am caught by the hunter who is chasing me. I beg you to put me into your book box so that I may escape. If I survive this crisis, I will do my utmost to repay your kindness."

Mr. Dongguo drew a long sigh. "It would go hard with me if the nobleman chasing you knew that I had tried to save you," he said. "However, I will abide by the Mohist principle and help you to escape death."

So saying, he emptied the book box and started to put the wolf into it. As he was careful not to injure the wolf's legs and tail, he was very slow in doing the job. The noise of the nobleman's chariot was drawing near, and the wolf was still outside the bag.

"There's no time to waste!" cried the wolf. "When

one is trying to put out a fire or save a drowning man, one does not care about polite manners. Do hurry up, please!"

The wolf bent its legs, and let the scholar tie them up. It arched its back, its head touching its tail, and turned its whole body into a round thing like a hedgehog. It was then easier for the scholar to cram it into the box. After closing the box, he lifted it back onto the back of the donkey. Then he withdrew with the donkey to the roadside, to wait for Zhao Jianzi to pass.

Soon the nobleman drove up. He stopped to ask the scholar if he had seen the wolf.

Mr. Dongguo said, "I have lost my way here, and have seen no trace of any wolf. There are so many branch roads and narrow paths around that it is really easy for a wolf to escape."

"Besides," he added after a pause, "though I am slow, I am not so stupid as not to understand the nature of a wolf. It is greedy and vicious; it never hesitates to do evil things. I would have done my best to help you catch it if I had seen it."

Zhao Jianzi thereupon turned his chariot around and drove along another road, followed by his men, dogs and hawks. Mr. Dongguo also started to go with his donkey, but in the opposite direction. Gradually the noise made by the nobleman's horses and followers died away.

"Please, sir," the wolf was heard saying in the box. "Do not forget to let me out of the box, untie my legs and pull out the arrow in my body."

But as soon as it had got out of the box, the wolf suddenly looked cruel and fierce. It shouted, "Just now you saved me. I am now very hungry and weak. I will soon die on the road to be torn to pieces by other animals. That will be far worse than to be killed, cooked and eaten by a noble family. You are a Mohist. Your principle is to make sacrifices for the benefit of the world. Why not at this moment sacrifice your body and let me have a good meal, to save me from starvation?"

It had hardly finished saying these words when

it leaped upon the old scholar, who, in great surprise, tried to fend off its attack with his arms, while withdrawing behind the donkey. Using the donkey as a barrier, the scholar circled around it to escape the wolf. Soon, both the wolf and the scholar were tired out, and both were gasping for breath, with the donkey between them.

"You are so ungrateful!" said the scholar. "You are so ungrateful!"

The wolf said, "Heaven has created people like you to be eaten by animals like me!"

By this time, the sun was setting. The old scholar was filled with fear, because he knew that other wolves would come when it was dark.

In the distance there appeared an old man walking toward them with a stick in his hand. At a glance Mr. Dongguo could tell that he was a wise and virtuous man. When he got near, Mr. Dongguo turned to kneel before him, and said in a tearful voice: "This wolf was being pursued by hunters when it saw me and begged me to save it. I did save it, but now it

wants to eat me, though I have been imploring it to be grateful. A fair word from you, sir, may save my life!"

While listening to the scholar's account, the old man sighed time and again. Beating the wolf with his stick, he said,

"You are wrong! What a shame it is to be so cruel to a man who has done you such a great favor. Confucianists say that even tigers and wolves do not betray one who has shown them kindness. What you have done shows you do not know this truth." Raising his voice, the old man commanded, "Go away quickly, or I will beat you to death with my stick!"

"Please listen to me for a while," the wolf said. "You know only one side of the story. There is an other side. When the scholar put me into his box, he tied my legs, pressed me with his books, and closed the box. I had to bend my body, unable to breathe freely. Then he had a lengthy conversation with Zhao Jianzi. It is easy to see that he intended to stifle me to death and have my flesh all for himself. That is why

I want to devour him."

A heated argument started between the scholar and the wolf, one trying to describe his sympathy for the wolf, and the other trying to prove the hard-heartedness of the scholar. Finally the old man suggested putting the wolf back into the box again, so that he could judge how much the wolf had suffered. To this both the scholar and the wolf agreed, and soon the wolf was in the box as it had been before.

"Have you got a knife with you?" the old man asked the scholar in a whisper.

The scholar said yes, and produced a small knife. The old man hinted with his eyes that he should kill the wolf. But the scholar hesitated. The old man then said,

"I know you are a humane man, but do not let your humaneness make you foolish. This ungrateful beast deserves death."

Together they used the knife to kill the wolf, which they threw to the roadside. After that, they parted and each went his own way.

The Lawsuit over an Egg

Once there was a man who was so poor that he did not know in the morning where he would find his supper in the evening. One day, he happened to pick up an egg on his way home. He was so excited that, on seeing his wife, he exclaimed, "I have got a fortune!"

"Where is it?" she asked, puzzled.

"Here it is!" he said loudly, holding the egg before her eyes. "But it will be years before my for tune materializes," he added.

Then he revealed to her what he was going to do. "I will put this egg under our neighbor's brooding hen. When all the eggs have been hatched, I will choose a hen from the chickens and bring it back. This hen will lay at least fifteen eggs a month, and I will have all of them hatched. Thus there will be many more hens and many more eggs. In two years I will have about three hundred chickens. I will sell them for ten pieces of gold. That amount of money is enough to buy five cows. Those cows will give birth to calves, and when the calves grow up, they will bear more calves. According to my calculations, I will have twenty-five calves in three years, and one hundred and fifty in six years. They will be worth three hundred pieces of gold. I will loan the money to other people at high rates of interest, and it will be easy to bring in five hundred pieces of gold in three years. Two-thirds of it will be spent on new land and houses, the rest on servants and concubines. We will then live a free and easy life. How happy we will be!"

But the wife, instead of feeling happy, became unbearably angry, because he had mentioned that he was going to buy concubines. She raised her hand and struck at the egg, which fell to the ground and broke. "I had better do away with the cause of all possible trouble right now!" she shouted.

The man flew into a rage and started beating his wife. He even dragged her to the local government

and begged the official there to punish her.

"This evil woman has ruined my fortune!" he cried. "Put her to death, please!"

"What fortune did you have?" the official asked. "How did she ruin it? "

The man then gave a detailed explanation of his plan, beginning from hatching the egg he had found and ending with buying servants and concubines.

"Such a large fortune was destroyed by one stroke of this evil woman's hand!" the official said. "She deserves death!" and he gave orders that the woman be boiled to death in hot water.

"No, no!" the woman cried. "What he said was only a dream. Nothing has happened. Why do you want to boil me?"

"Your husband wanted to buy concubines, but that did not happen - it was only a dream. Why were you jealous?"

"Of course that did not happen," said the woman. "But the sooner the cause of the trouble is removed, the better."

At this, the official laughed, and set her free.

S T O R I E S   O F

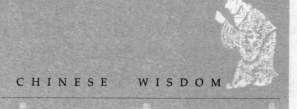

CHINESE   WISDOM

图书在版编目（CIP）数据

中国古典智慧 ／ 丁往道编译.
－北京：外文出版社，2007
ISBN 978-7-119-03404-1

I. 中... II. 丁... III. 英语—对照读物，故事—英、汉
IV. H319.4:I
中国版本图书馆 CIP 数据核字（2005）第 066636 号

责任编辑：杨春燕
封面设计：华子图文
印刷监制：张国祥

外文出版社网址：
　http://www.flp.com.cn
外文出版社电子信箱：
　info@flp.com.cn
　sales@flp.com.cn

中国古典智慧

丁往道　编译

＊

© 外文出版社
外文出版社出版
（中国北京百万庄大街 24 号）
邮政编码　100037
北京外文印刷厂印刷
中国国际图书贸易总公司发行
（中国北京车公庄西路 35 号）
北京邮政信箱第 399 号　邮政编码　100044
2007 年(32 开)第 1 版
2008 年第 1 版第 2 次印刷
（英）
ISBN 978-7-119-03404-1
04400
10-EC-3582P